TOTAL GUITAR

MAKING YOU A BETTER GUITARIST

6 CLASSIC TRACKS

SULTANS OF SWING
DIRE STRAITS
*Plus...*five more classic hit songs

This publication is not authorised for sale in
the United States of America and/or Canada

Wise Publications
London/ New York/ Sydney/ Paris/ Copenhagen/ Madrid
www.internetmusicshop.com

TOTAL GUITAR

Exclusive Distributors:
Music Sales Limited
8/9 Frith Street, London W1V 5TZ, England.

Music Sales Pty Limited
120 Rothschild Avenue, Rosebery, NSW 2018, Australia.

Order No. AM956472
ISBN 0-7119-7465-9
This book © Copyright 1999 by Wise Publications

Cover and Book Design By Nicholas Ellis
Music Engraving by Digital Music Art

Photographs courtesy of Redferns, London Features International and Rex Features.
Printed in the United Kingdom by Caligraving Limited, Thetford, Norfolk.

Your Guarantee of Quality
As publishers, we strive to produce every book to the highest standards. This book has been carefully designed to minimise
awkward page turns and to make playing from it a real pleasure.
Particular care has been given to specifying acid-free, neutral-sized paper made from pulps which have not been elemental
chlorine bleached. This pulp is from farmed sustainable forests and was produced with special regard for the environment. The
printing and binding have been planned to ensure a sturdy, attractive publication which should give years of enjoyment.
If your copy fails to meet our high standards, please inform us and we will gladly replace it.

Music Sales' complete catalogue describes thousands of titles and is available in full colour by subject, direct from Music Sales
Limited. Please state your areas of interest and send a cheque/ postal order for £1.50 for postage to: Music Sales Limited,
Newmarket Road, Bury St. Edmunds, Suffolk IP33 3YB.

www.internetmusicshop.com

Hello, I'm Harry Wylie, the editor of Total Guitar, the country's best-selling and most popular guitar magazine. Welcome to a brand new series of music books which are based on TG's hugely popular Classic Track series.

Over the past five years, my magazine has featured one classic guitar song per issue in all its glorious detail, for readers to learn, play and jam with over a CD backing track. Only the most requested guitar moments have been chosen, featuring some of the most famous guitarists and artists in the world - from Hendrix to Clapton, The Stone Roses to The Beatles and Dire Straits to the Manic Street Preachers - and six of them are featured in this book.

This exciting new series from Music Sales brings you the highlights of the last five years of Total Guitar - I really hope you enjoy them! And if you do, why not pick up a copy of Total Guitar every month... Be seeing you!

How to use the CD

On the TG CD you'll find demonstration versions and backing tracks for each of the six tracks in this book. Listen to the audio in conjunction with the music and TAB in the book, and you'll soon be playing along! If you're not sure how to read TAB, check out our one-page guide at the back of this book.

Sometimes the demo version is split up across several tracks to let you skip straight to the section you're interested in - refer to the verse and chorus markings in the music to identify each section.

Timing boxes are given for each transcription to help you find your way around - these always refer to the backing track, and may not always match up with the demonstration versions.

This Enhanced CD can be played on your hi-fi or on your multimedia PC. If you are on the Internet and want to browse the World's largest selection of sheet music, simply place the CD in your CD-Rom drive and follow the on-screen instructions. **TG**

Further reading ...

If you're a fan of TG Classic Tracks, then why not check out some of the other book and CD titles available from Music Sales.

The 'Play Guitar With ...' series is the biggest range of CD books for guitarists currently available - allowing you to play along with more than 30 of the world's most famous bands and artists.

Each book contains full TAB, standard notation, lyrics and chord symbols, plus a specially recorded CD containing full demonstration versions of each track, and professional 'soundalike' backing tracks.

Here's a small selection of the titles available:

AC/DC
Order No. AM955900

the kinks
Order No. AM951863

the beatles
Order No. NO90665

kula shaker
Order No. AM943767

the beatles Book 2
Order No. NO90667

john lennon
Order No. AM943756

blur
Order No. AM935320

bob marley
Order No. AM937739

bon jovi
Order No. AM92558

metallica
Order No. AM92559

eric clapton
Order No. AM950862

alanis morissette
Order No. AM943723

phil collins
Order No. AM928147

oasis
Order No. AM943712

the cranberries
Order No. AM941699

elvis presley
Order No. AM937090

dire straits
Order No. DG70735

pulp
Order No. AM938124

david gilmour
Order No.AM954602

sting
Order No. AM928092

buddy holly
Order No. AM943734

the stone roses
Order No. AM943701

john lee hooker
Order No. AM951885

the stone roses Book 2
Order No. AM955890

b.b. king
Order No. AM951874

paul weller
Order No. AM937827

All these titles are available from your local music shop, and can also be ordered over the internet by visiting the Music Sales website at www.internetmusicshop.com.

Back In Black

AC/DC

AC/DC have created many text book rock tunes. The Total Guitar team don their school uniforms, and look for the chalk...

Tips

The riffs

The opening riff perfectly embodies the AC/DC concept – three repeating chords (E, D and A) interspersed with single note licks. The chords emphasise beats one and three, using silences to create a sense of drama. The first fill descends the E blues scale while the second fill has the whole band playing the chromatically ascending notes against a pedal B note. This second fill is varied later (at 2:50) incorporating its chromatic pedal tone figure into a new riff. For the chorus sections, power chords are syncopated by both guitars locking into a groove with the drums to create a driving swing.

The solo

For his solos Angus bases his playing on the E blues scale using different note articulations (vibrato, bends, slides, hammer-ons and pull-offs) for variety. His tendency to take a few specific licks and turn them into 'hooks' is evident here – check the opening four bars of the first solo where he descends from E to C# over a low E note pedal. Also the start of his second solo picks up on the diad figures that closed his first solo. There's some great playing here, so dig in!

Angus Young - for those about to rock, we salute you!

THE guitar nucleus of AC/DC is formed by the brothers Angus and Malcolm Young who started the band in 1973. With lead guitar duties taken by 'school boy' Angus and rhythm guitar to Malcolm, they have always had a boogie blues-based rock approach to making music. Angus states: "Our musical ambition is to put down a whole album like it was done by Little Richard back in the '50s... we may be little but we make a lot of noise."

After the international success of their *Highway To Hell* (1979) album and the death of singer Bon Scott, AC/DC released *Back In Black* (1980) with new vocalist Brian Johnson. This resulted in, among others, the classic title track with its memorable twin guitar arrangement and trademark guitar solos.

THE AC/DC SOUND

One of the main characteristics of the AC/DC sound is the markedly different tones of Angus and Malcolm Young. Angus uses a Gibson SG with a Marshall JTM 45 amp through vintage 4x12 cabinets while Malcolm uses a '63 Gretsch Firebird (one Filter'tron in the bridge position) with a Marshall JTM 100 amp through vintage 4x12 cabinets. Angus' tone is the dirtiest of the two but their punch is achieved more through sheer volume than amp gain. To achieve this, select a moderately overdriven tone from your amp/effects pedal, boost the bass frequencies slightly, and dig in hard with your plectrum. Finally, put on your blazer, tie and cap and get ready to rock! **TG**

Back In Black

Words & Music by Angus Young, Malcolm Young & Brian Johnson

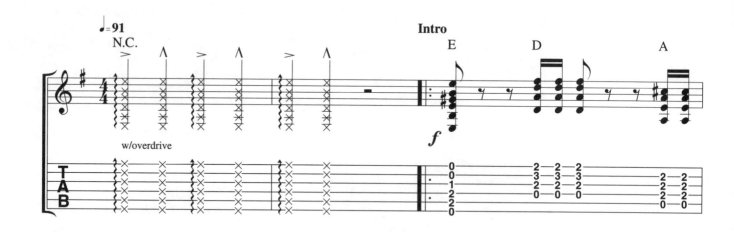

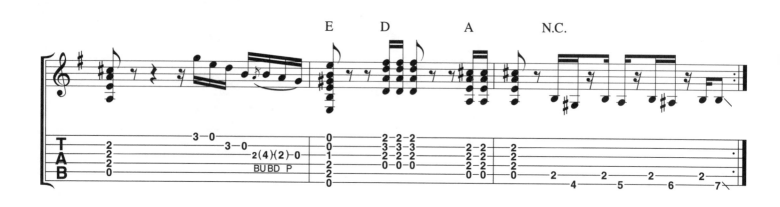

Verse

1. Back in___ black,___ I hit the sack, I been too long,___ I'm glad___ to be___ back. (Yes I
2. Back in the back of a cad-il-lac, number one with a bul-let, I'm a pow-er pack. (Yes I

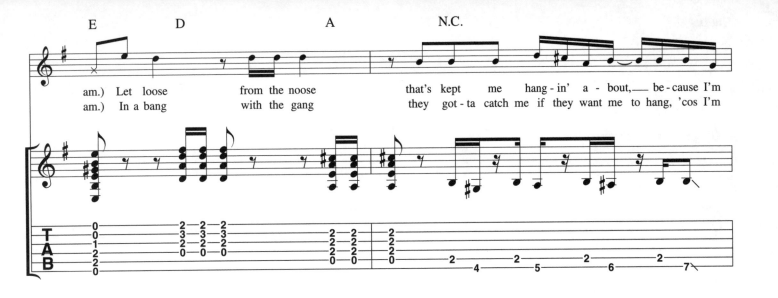

am.) Let loose from the noose that's kept me hang-in' a - bout,— be-cause I'm
am.) In a bang with the gang they got - ta catch me if they want me to hang, 'cos I'm

liv - in' like a star,— 'cos it's get-tin' me— high for - get the hearse 'cos I'll ne-ver die! I got
back on the track and I'm beat-ing the— flack, no - bo-dy's gon-na get me on an-oth-er rap. So

nine lives, cat's eyes, los - in' ev' - ry one of them and run - nin' wild, 'cos I'm
look at me now, I'm just mak-in' my play, don't try to push your luck, just get out of my way, 'cos I'm

Solo

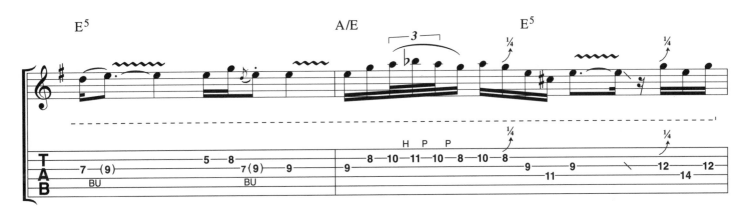

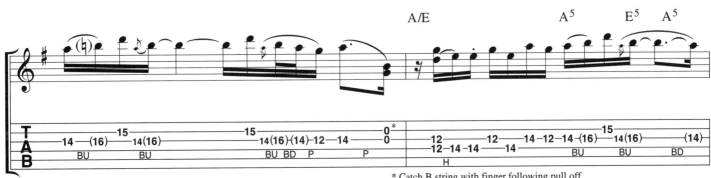

* Catch B string with finger following pull off

Fill 1

Gtr. 2 (elec.)

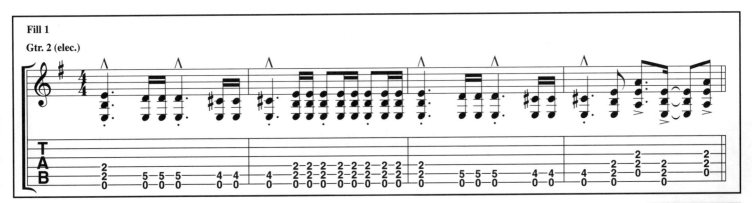

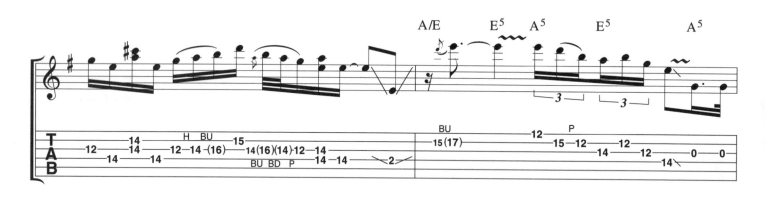

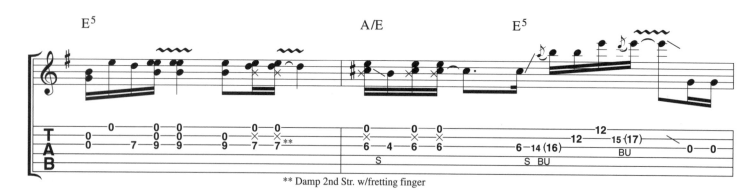

** Damp 2nd Str. w/fretting finger

D.%. al Coda
(No repeats)

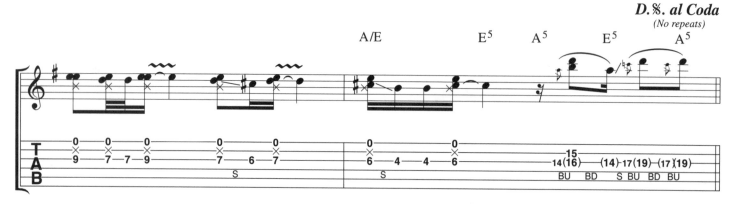

✛ *Coda*

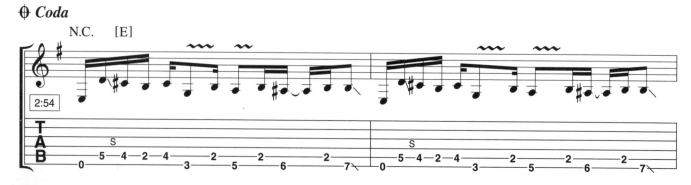

[A]

[E]

Well, I'm——

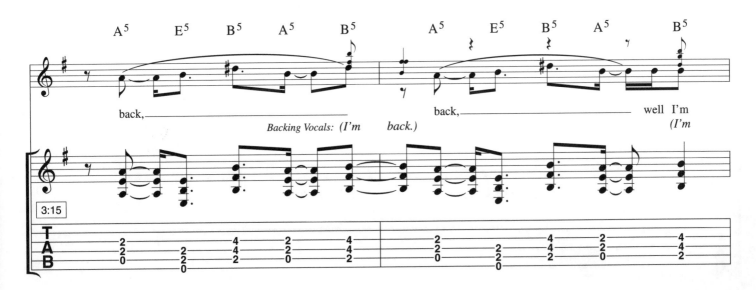

back,——————————————
Backing Vocals: (I'm   back.)

back,——————————— well I'm
(I'm

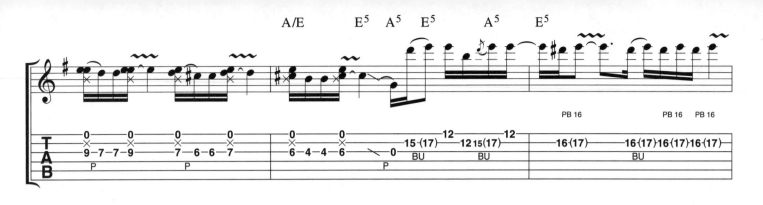

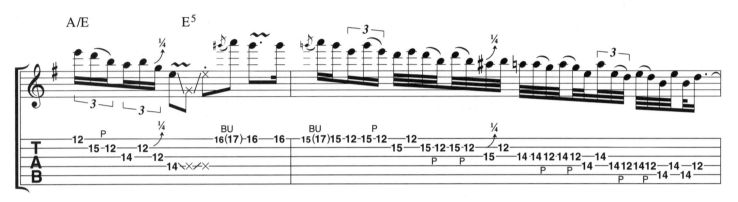

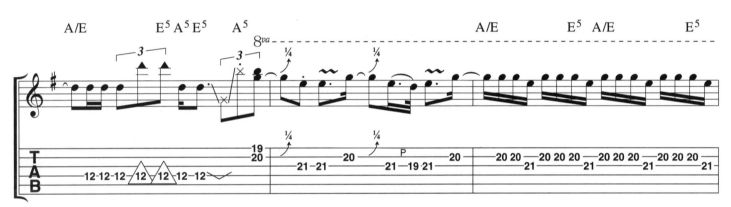

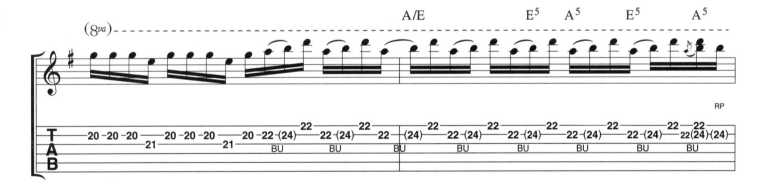

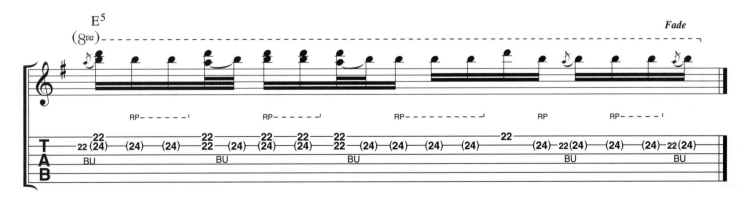

White Room

CREAM

Learn how to play this 1968 rock classic, with a full transcription for single electric guitar.

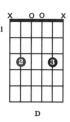

T G **Fretboxes**

Gm

F

Dm

C

Am7

D

D

Shown here are all the chords from Eric's rhythm guitar part (the first five are the distortion part from the intro, though you'll also notice from the tab that we've notated the intro's harmony guitars on a single stave so they can be played on one guitar). Use the D minor pentatonic scale at the 10th position for the answering phrases and outro solo. The final verse's lead guitar part uses the D major pentatonic scale in places at the 14th fret position.

Cream - Eric Clapton riffing with his Gibson 335.

WHITE *Room* was an unusual Cream track because it owed less to blues than some of their work (e.g. *Crossroads*, *Sunshine Of Your Love* and even *Politician*). It's based on a major chord sequence – D, C and G, which moves via B♭ and C before looping. Apart from the repeated intro and bridge sections, it's possible to solo over the sequence just using the scales of Dm pentatonic and Dmaj pentatonic. We've included the harmony guitars on the backing so you can play the main chord part.

Clapton was using a Gibson 335 into two Marshall heads. For the main (non-wah) guitar, use a mild overdrive, with higher gain for the solos. Eric used to have two amps, with one set up especially for lead, so he could

T G **Additional lyrics**

Verse 4

**At the party she was kindness in the hard crowd,
Consolation for the old wound now forgotten,
Yellow tigers crouched in jungles in her dark eyes,
She's just dressing, goodbye windows, tired starlings.**

preset the solo tone to perfection. So obviously if you're going to play the song live, you'll have to carry two Marshall stacks around. Sorry, but that's just the only way you'll get that tone, man… T G

White Room

Words & Music by Jack Bruce & Pete Brown

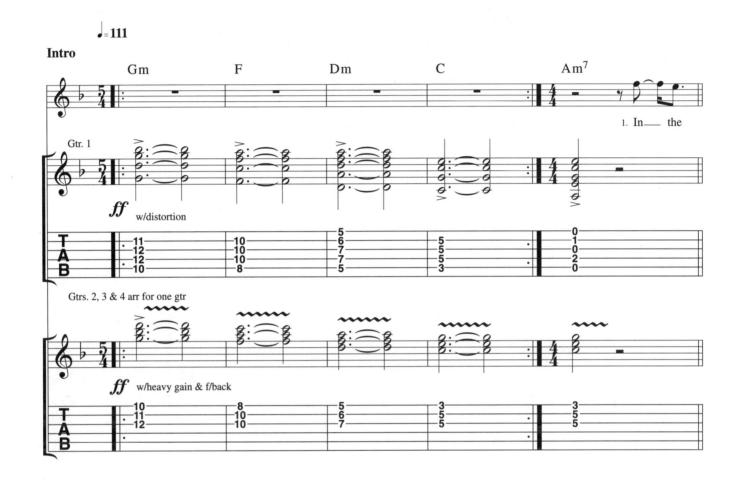

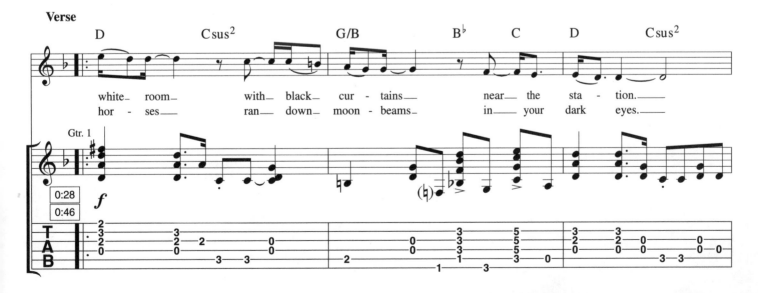

Black roofed coun - try, no gold pave - ments, tired
Dawn light smiles on you leav - ing my con -

star - lings.
- tent - ment.

2. Sil - ver I'll

wait in this place where the sun ne - ver

Gtr. 1

1:03

Gtr 2

w/wah wah

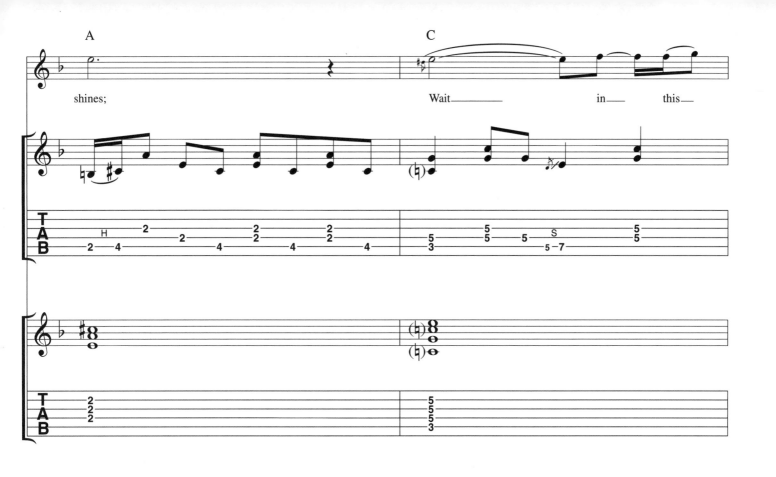

shines;   Wait_____   in__ this__

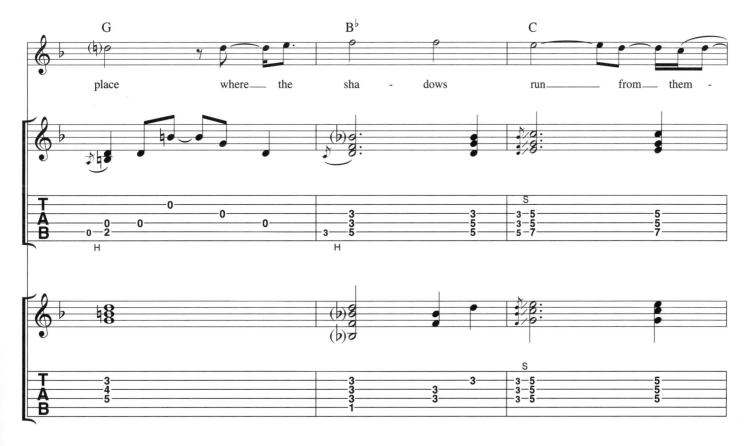

place   where__ the   sha - dows   run_____ from__ them -

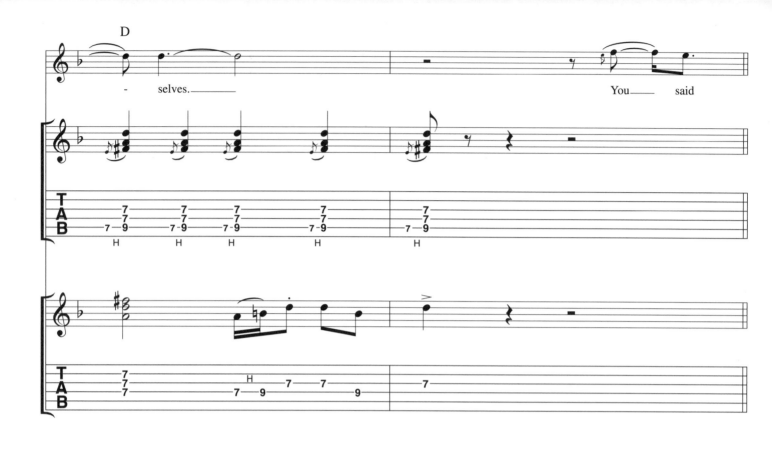

Verse

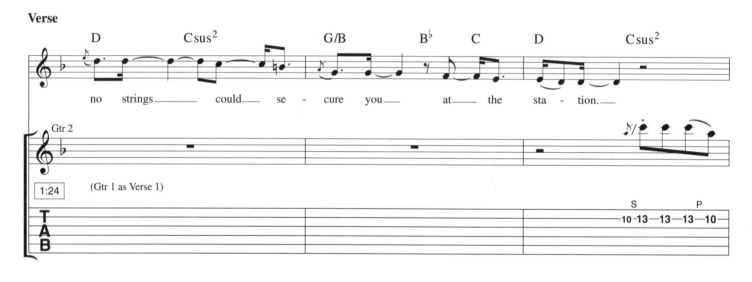

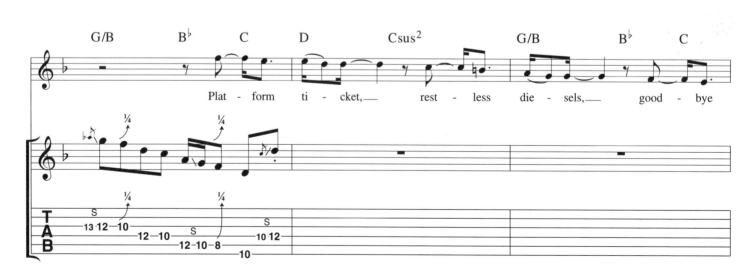

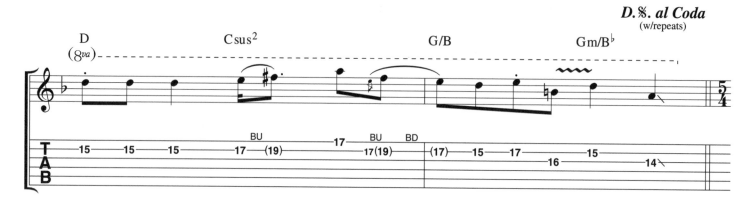

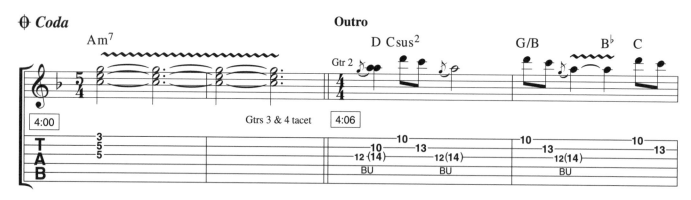

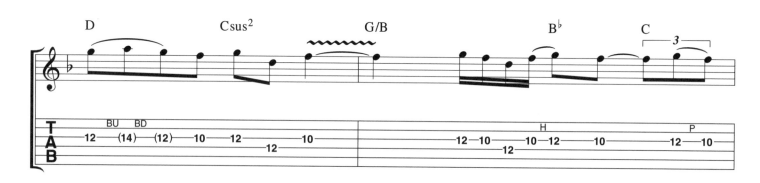

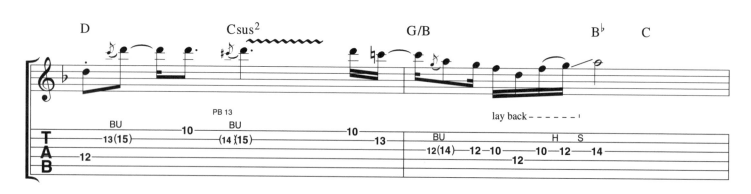

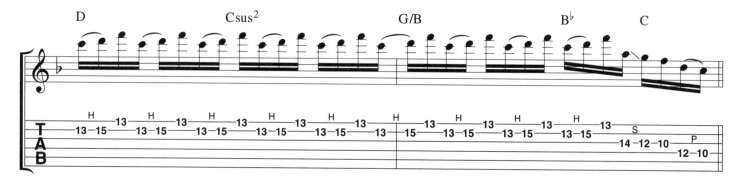

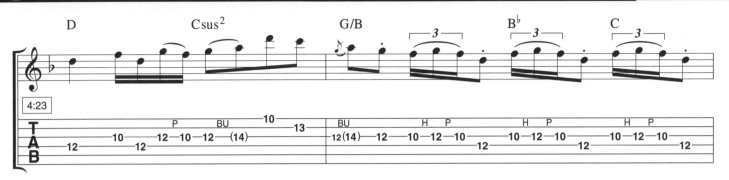

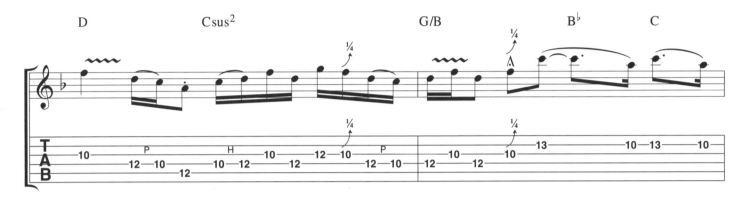

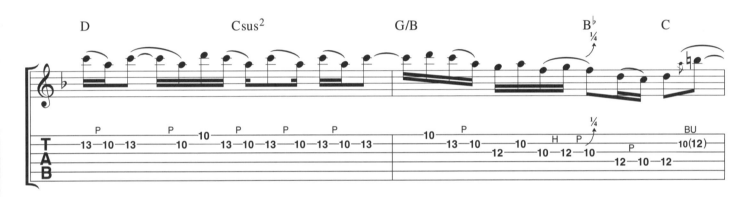

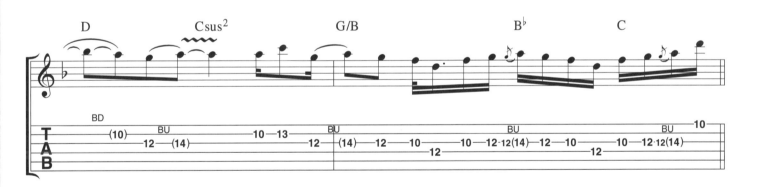

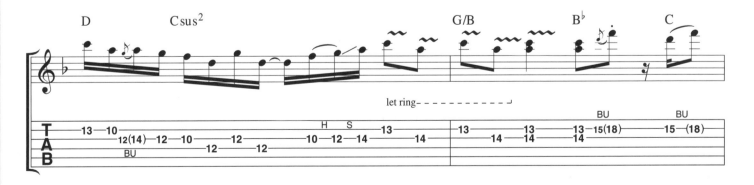

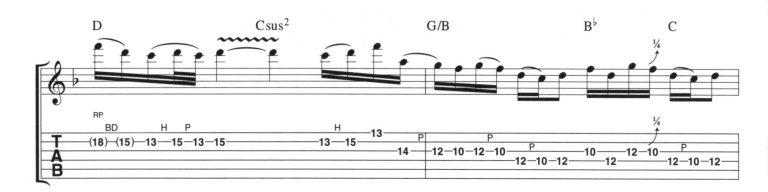

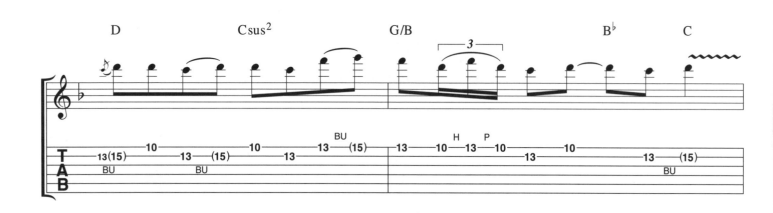

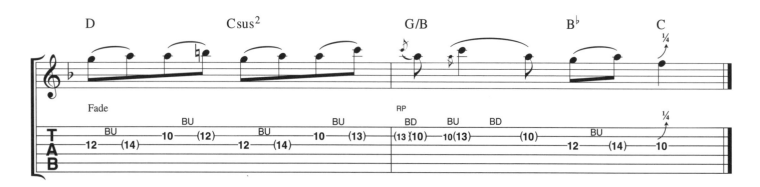

On the CD

TRACK 5
Intro, then verses 1 & 2

TRACK 6
The main chorus riff

TRACK 7
Verses 3 & 4, into chorus 2

TRACK 8
Verse 5, into chorus 3

TRACK 9
The first complete guitar solo, followed by chorus 4

TRACK 10
Verse 6, then chorus 5

TRACK 11
The second guitar solo

TRACK 12
Backing track only

Fretboxes

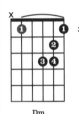
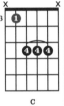

Dm   C

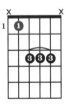
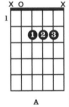

Bb   A

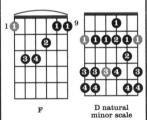

F   D natural minor scale

Shown here are all the chord shapes you need for the rhythm part.

The D natural minor scale shape at the 9th fret can be used for improvising a solo.

Sultans Of Swing

DIRE STRAITS

This 1978 single is <u>the</u> most requested track by TG readers. Enjoy our full transcription of what is, frankly, a classic amongst classics...

Mark Knopfler - The definitive 'Sultan Of Swing'!

CONSIDERING the year in which it was released, *Sultans Of Swing* was an odd candidate for a platinum-selling trans-Atlantic top ten single. It was recorded at the height of Punk in the UK, by a then-unknown band, there's no chorus lyric, and it tells a long and involved story.

But succeed it did – largely due to the subtle and lyrical playing of guitarist Mark Knopfler. His clean compressed tone and fingerstyle technique instantly defined a 'new' Strat sound which has, with a only few exceptions, remained his own.

TECHNIQUE & SOUND

Although you can just about get through the song with a plectrum, it's worth learning it fingerstyle. You *can* improvise the lead, but there are some parts which your gig audience will expect to hear – notably the "time bell" chord (page 38), and the outro arpeggios (page 41). Play these with thumb and first finger – it's the only way to get the speed.

Knopfler was one of the first players (apart from the ubiquitous Jimi Hendrix) to use a Strat's 'in-between' setting – *i.e.* two single-coil pickups together. His sound was one of the reasons Fender began fitting 5-way, rather than 3-way switches on Strats. This position is often referred to as 'out-of-phase' (which is technically incorrect) or 'wired in parallel' (which is deadly dull). Whichever, the resultant tone is thinner than a normal Strat, but with lots of treble and bass. The guitar on *Sultans Of Swing* uses neck and middle pickups, through compressor, reverb, and very subtle overdrive. On the 'chorus' riff Mark, appropriately enough, switches in a chorus pedal. The effect is quite thick, almost to the point of implying another guitar, so set the 'width' control fairly high.

SULTAN OF SONGWRITING

The song was not composed on the Strat, Mark recalls; "The first version was written on a National acoustic, which had been open-tuned. It was a totally different song. But when I got the Strat in 1977, the song completely changed. It's an interesting example of how sometimes just playing on another instrument, or with a different tuning, dictates something different to you."

And what's that lyric all about? "It was a pub jazz band that I saw in the mid-seventies – they were actually called the Sultans Of Swing. The song is the story of their aspirations – these people could have settled for ordinary day jobs, but they chose musical freedom, which is so much better than just letting your life waste away." I think we can all agree with that! **TG**

Sultans Of Swing

Words & Music by Mark Knopfler

Chorus

Lon - don town.—

1:19

(spoken:) You check out

Verse 3

Gui - tar George, he knows all the chords.—

1:32

Mind, he's stric - tly rhy - thm he does - n't want to make it cry—

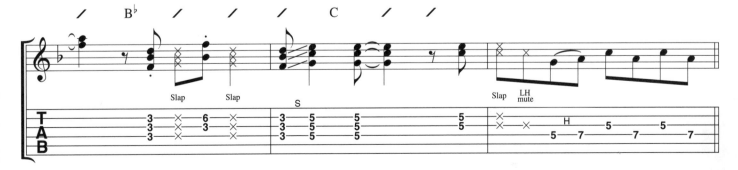

Verse 4

Chorus

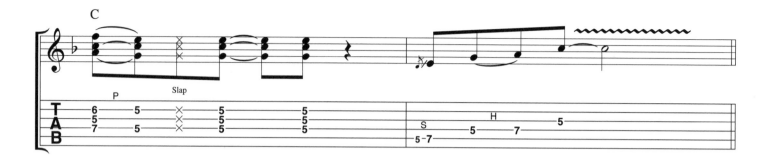

Verse 6

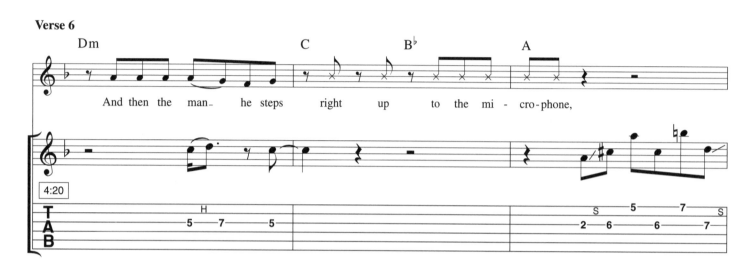

And then the man— he steps right up to the mi - cro-phone,

`4:20`

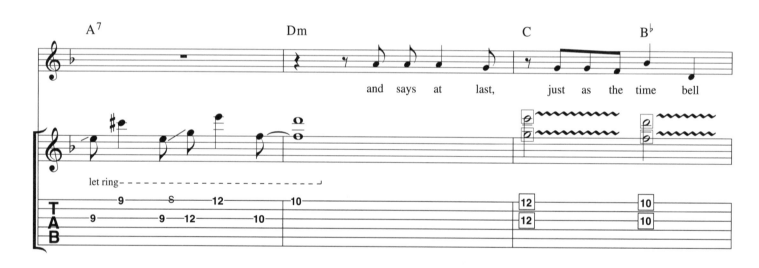

and says at last, just as the time bell

let ring -

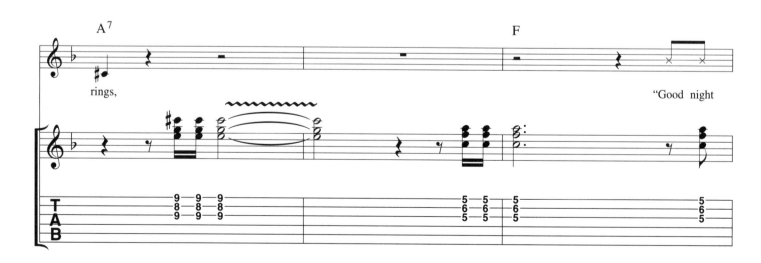

rings, "Good night

Chorus

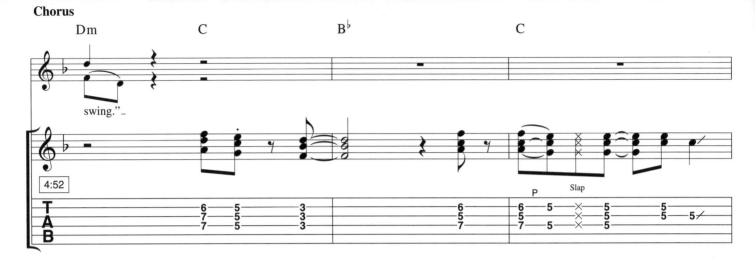

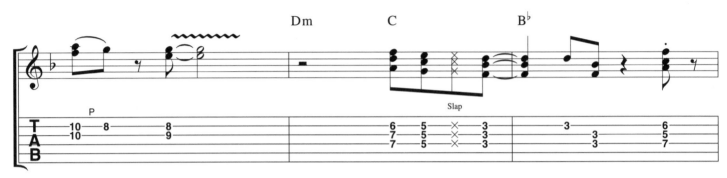

Solo 2

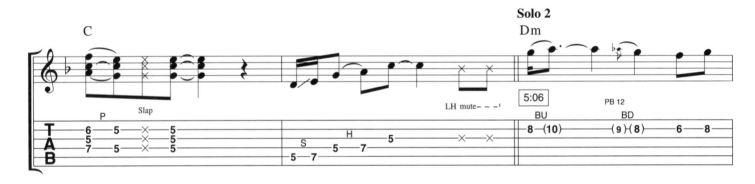

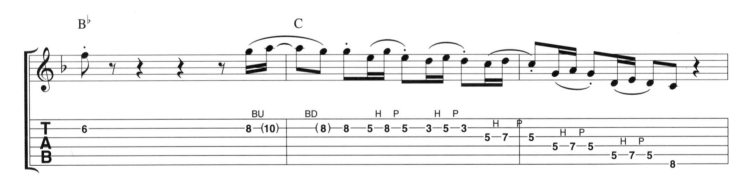

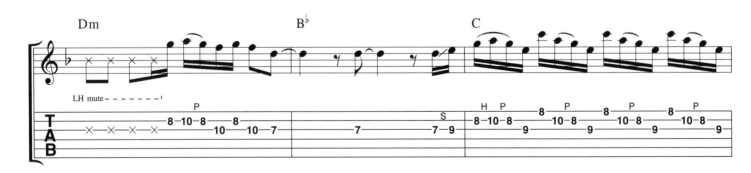

TG On the CD

TRACK 13
12-bar intro

TRACK 14
Verse and chorus 12-bar sequence

TRACK 15
The solo in full

TRACK 16
Backing track only

TG Fretboxes

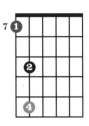

B riff shape

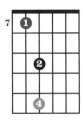

E riff shape

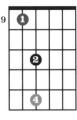

F# riff shape

The basic rhythm guitar accompaniment to the verses uses the three shapes shown above. The note in a lighter grey is added on every third downstroke, then taken off again for the fourth - it's that familiar 'der-der-dah-der' lick so beloved of Status Quo. It's a simple riff to play but can be a little tricky while singing as well so don't be fooled by its apparent simplicity!

Johnny B. Goode

CHUCK BERRY

This 1958 rocker is one song that <u>every</u> guitarist has to know. To quote Michael J. Fox from Back To The Future - "Alright guys, listen, this is a blues riff in B. Watch me for the changes and try to keep up, okay?"

Chuck Berry - He knows a thing or two about rock n' roll!

IF ever there was such a thing as a 'rock 'n' roll standard', *Johnny B Goode* is the one. It's one of those riffs that will always inspire a pub full of people to enjoy the band's encore. Contrary to popular belief, Chuck Berry didn't actually play the classic 4-bar intro on the original Chess recording, but we figured that you'd want to have a go at this famous section, so our transcription is a compiled version devised for one guitarist, using the essential parts of each line.

BLUES IN B
The original track is in B♭ major (or fairly close to it) but we've nudged the key up to B for two reasons. Firstly, it's a more guitarist-friendly key – Chuck was heavily influenced by his piano player, Johnnie Johnson, and so often played in B♭ and E♭ because they are more keyboard-based. Secondly, it was common practice in the late '50s to alter the tape speed quite substantially – you'll find that you can't easily play along to Berry's original if you work with normal A440 tuning, so it's debatable which key the song was originally in.

Interestingly, it's played with a slight 'swing' rhythm, not only from the double bass and drums but also from the intro guitar part. We've notated the track using straight eighth notes, which is how most bands play it live, but you may find it interesting to try out a different rhythmic slant.

GUITAR SOUND
There is a tiny bit of amp overdrive on both guitars in the original recording, although the riffs sound perfectly fine with heavier levels of drive, if that's your preference - check out Jimi Hendrix's version if you need further proof (On *Hendrix Live In The West*). Chuck used a Gibson ES-350T (a semi-acoustic f-hole guitar fitted with two humbucking pickups) through a tweed-covered Fender amp – even he doesn't remember the exact model, although he now uses the Fender Dual Showman Reverb on stage. He never uses effects – his attitude to rock 'n' roll guitar was summed up in a recent interview; "I tried a wah-wah once. Stubbed my toe on it. Forget it."

Michael J. Fox was right, the kids loved this tune! **TG**

Johnny B. Goode
Words & Music by Chuck Berry

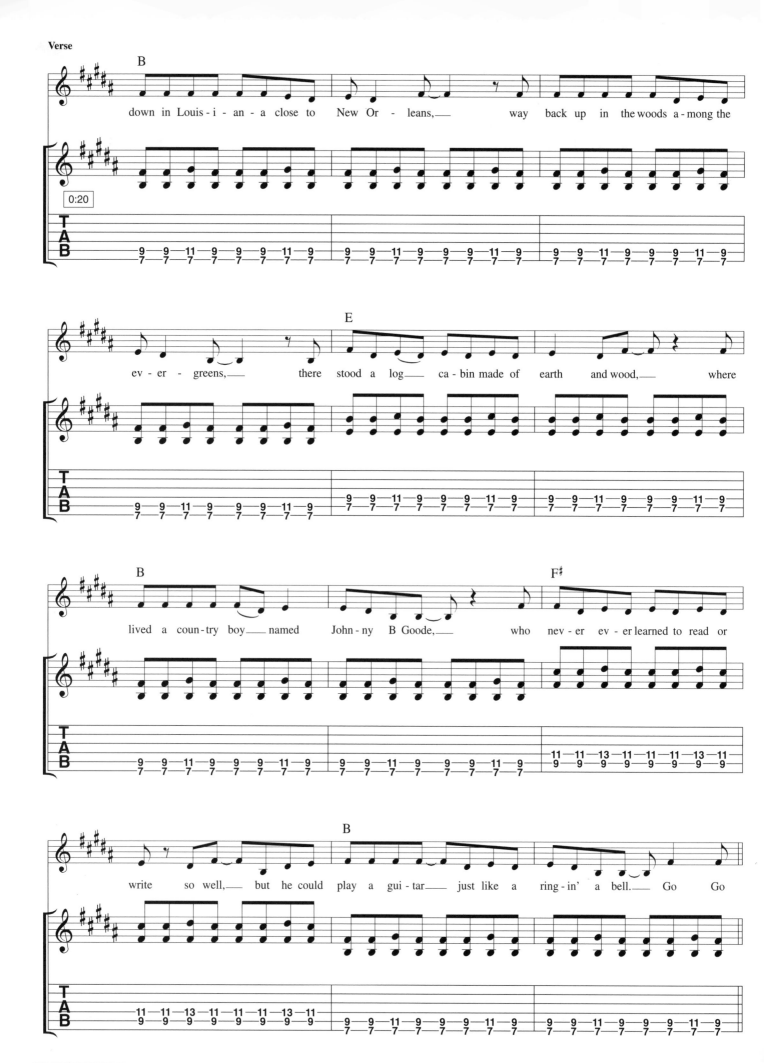

Chorus

On the CD

TRACK 17
a. Intro riff
b. Verse accompaniment

TRACK 18
a. Chorus, without repeats
b. Bridge

TRACK 19
a. First guitar solo
b. Last chorus & outro solo

TRACK 20
Backing track only

Fretboxes

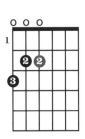

riff (open)

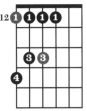

riff 12th fret

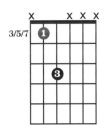

C5, D5, E5

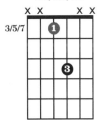

F5, G5, A5

The main riff is doubled in two octaves, using the open position and 12th fret position shown. Start on one of the higher E notes shown in black, then play either riff as shown in the tab.
The accompaniment is almost entirely based on two-note power chords – shown here are two suggested shapes. All non-fretted strings should be muted with the picking hand.

Wishing Well

FREE

This 1972 single features one of the most famous low slung, downright sexy rock riffs ever. Prepare to wow the audience!

Free - One of the greatest rock bands ever? The man from TG, he say 'YES'!

WISHING Well appeared on Free's final studio album, *Heartbreaker*. Guitarist Paul Kossoff, increasingly plagued by ill-health, played on only five of the tracks; all the guitar parts on *Wishing Well* were actually by singer Paul Rodgers, himself a very competent (and under-rated) guitarist. There are three guitars on the original – two rhythm and one lead – and they are all transcribed here.

Most of the lead passages are deliberately unmelodic, to compliment the fluid style of the vocal – some are only one or two notes, so feel free to improvise when you're not playing the accompaniment parts. Oddly, the playing sounds very much like Kossoff, even though we are assured it isn't! As for guitar sound, use heavy overdrive and the bridge pickup, with optional phasing on the lead part. Turn on, tune up and get Free… **TG**

Wishing Well

Words & Music by Paul Rodgers, Simon Kirke, Tetsu Yamauchi, John Bundrick & Paul Kossoff

Verse

Chorus

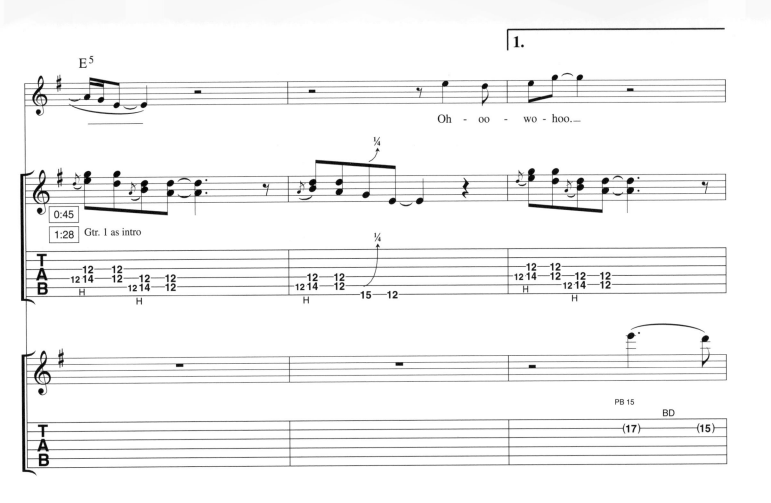

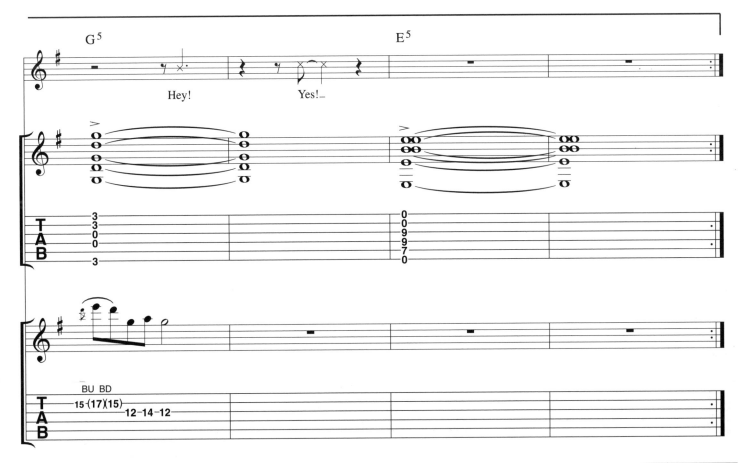

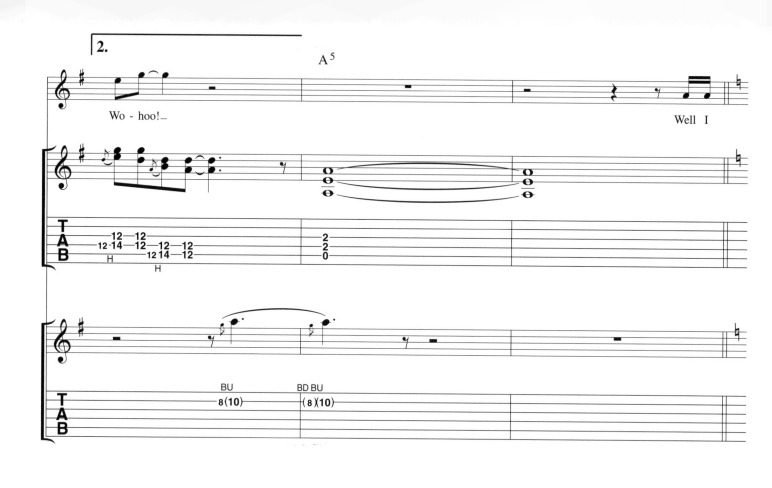

Bridge

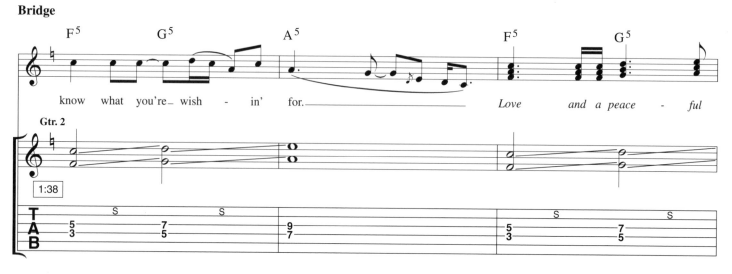

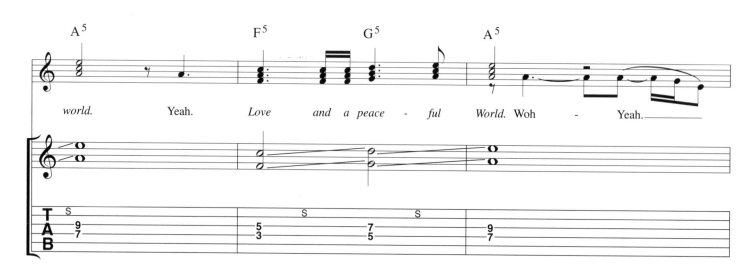

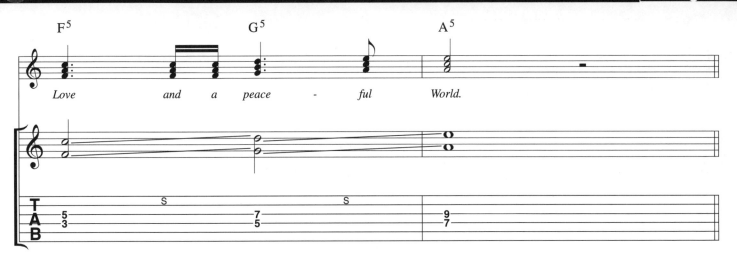

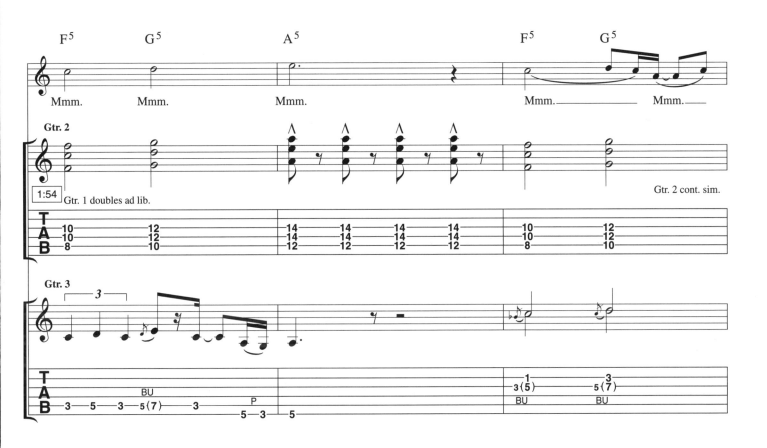

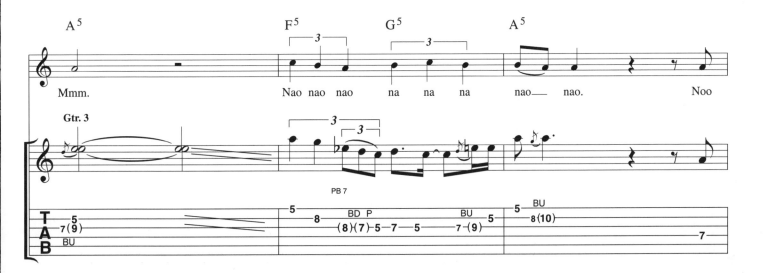

A

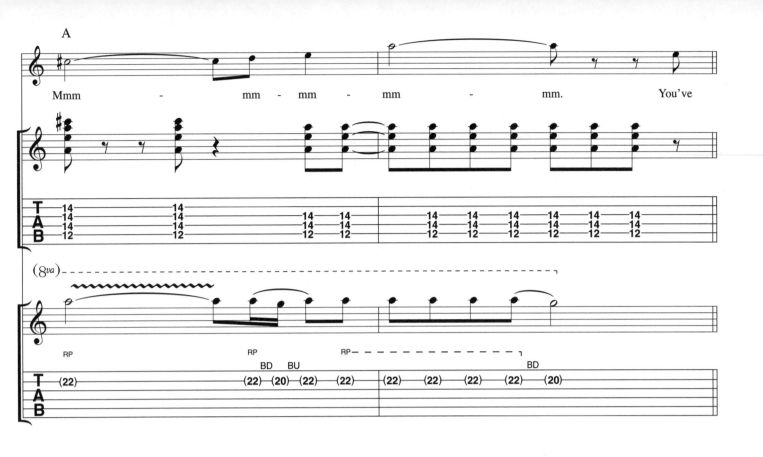

Mmm - mm - mm - mm - mm.   You've

Chorus/Outro

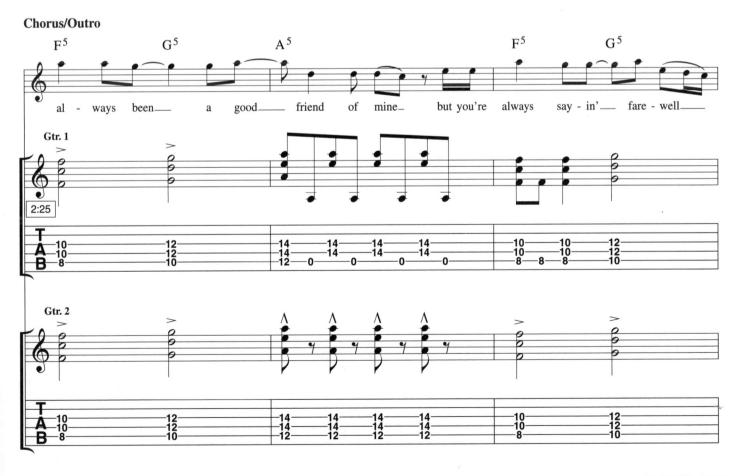

al - ways been___ a good___ friend of mine___ but you're always say - in'___ fare - well___

Samba Pa Ti

SANTANA

Total Guitar explains how to play this famous Latin style instrumental single from 1970.

Fretboxes

G major pos 1

G major pos 2

G major pos 3

G major pos 4

Most of the improvised solo is made up of notes from the pentatonic scale or the G major scale shown here. It's almost all 'diatonic' - i.e. all the notes relate the home key, though there are times where chromatic passing tones can also be used.

Santana - Playing himself into music history with his PRS.

SAMBA PA TI appeared on Santana's second album, *Abraxas,* which is still regarded by many as his finest work. In addition to *Samba Pa Ti*, the album also featured a 'Classic cover' in the form of Peter Green's excellent *Black Magic Woman.*

The song is played entirely in the key of G, and after the first intro theme has been played twice, there is an 8-bar bridge passage, then the main track comes in. From this point on, the whole track consists of G and Am, so it's very easy to improvise over using the G major pentatonic or G major scales (see fretboxes).

MUSICAL SHOCKWAVES

Santana's style (apparently) relies on a mystical feeling called "Duende" found in flamenco music, a sensation best described as 'musical shockwaves in the soul'. In more practical terms, he has a very fluid sense of timing, and will often repeat musical lines with subtly different phrasing. He rarely uses vibrato on the top bends, so your bending will have to be very accurate to stay in tune with the backing, although it has be said that Carlos' own intonation misses the mark on more than one occasion! Take note of the unison bends in the transcription - these are another Santana characteristic that are fairly easy to

achieve. Just fret a note on the first string, together with a note three frets higher on the second string then bend that note up until both strings are the same pitch. The result is a warbling screech which is very effective at bringing out specific notes in your solos.

GUITAR SOUND

For the *Abraxas* album, Carlos used three Les Pauls through a Fender Princeton which had been souped up by Randall Smith (later of Boogie fame) to include an extra gain stage. The guitar sound on *Samba Pa Ti* was a refinished wine red Les Paul with the middle pickup position selected, through the Princeton.

To create a Santana style sound, use either the neck or middle pickup position (if you're playing a Strat, back off the tone to about half), with a warm overdrive sound. Pick fairly gently - he's not an aggressive player - and make sure the distortion isn't so thick that you lose plectrum attack. That way, you can control the level of drive (and therefore the tone) purely by how you pick the notes.

And a final word for those of you who say that *Samba Pa Ti* is played out of tune, out of time, and with a very dubious sense of pitch, I say; maybe so, but *you* didn't write it, did you? **TG**

Samba Pa-Ti

By Carlos Santana

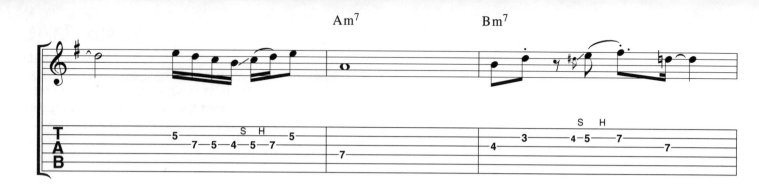

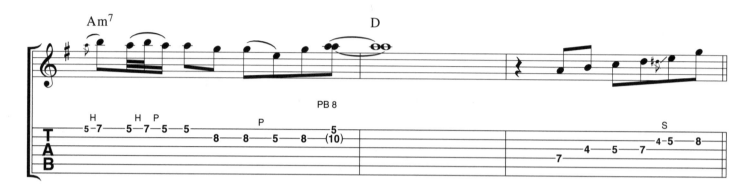

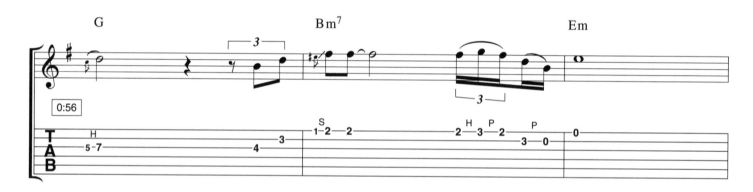

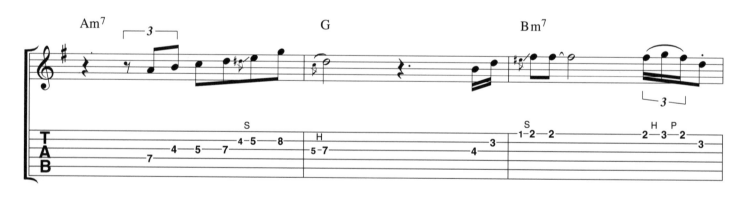

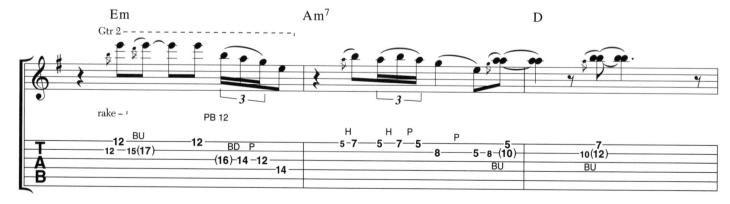

** Gtr 2 bend B string only

** Gtr 2 bend B string only

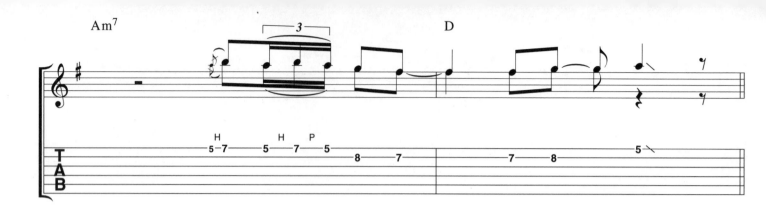

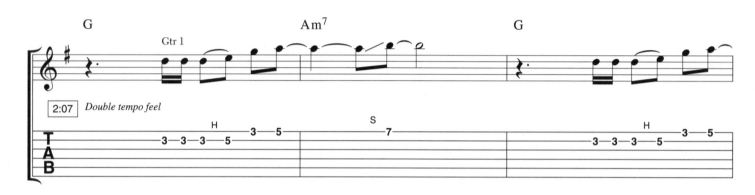

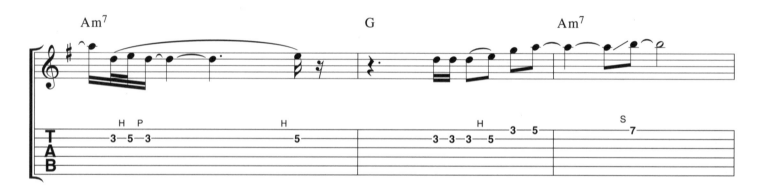

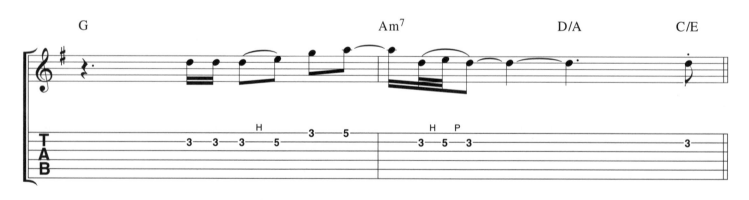

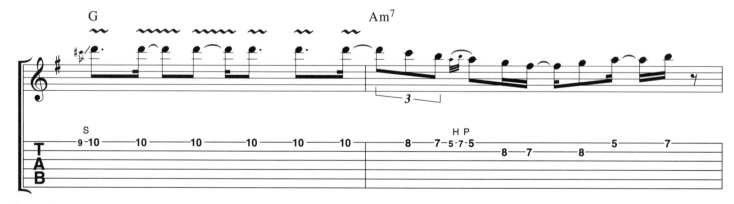

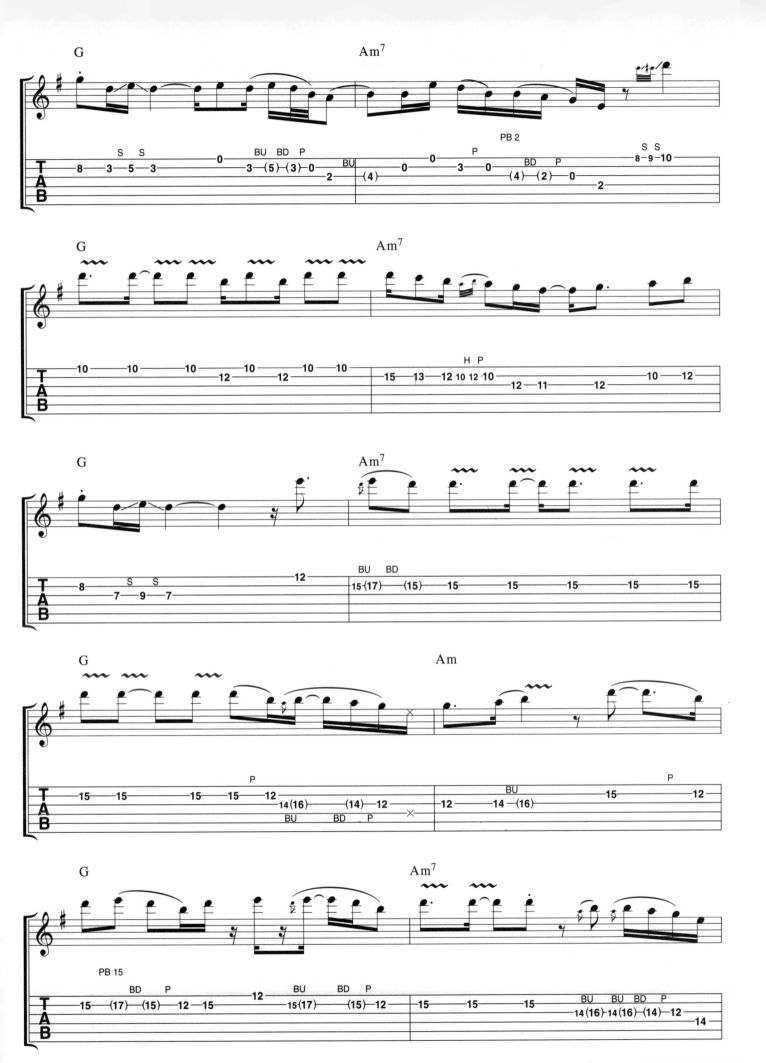

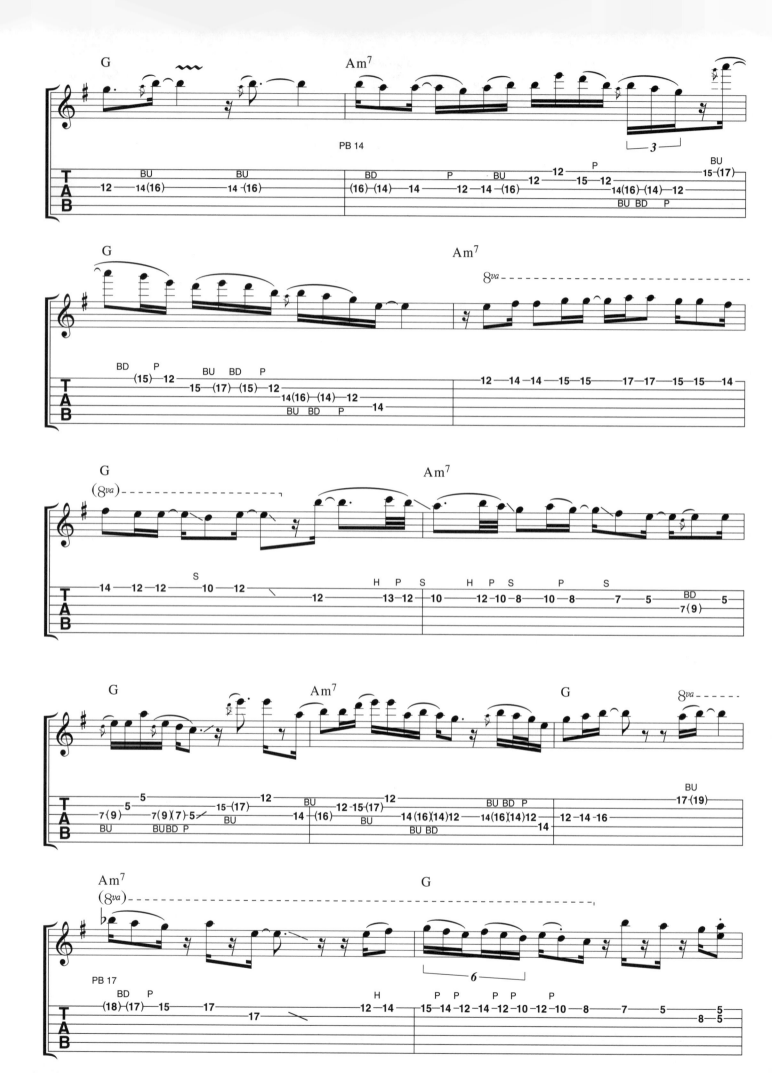

NOTATION AND TABLATURE

The Total Guitar tab and notation system covers all the commonly used guitar techniques, and is designed to be as easy to read as possible. The examples shown here explain what it all means…

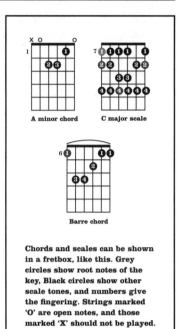

A minor chord   C major scale

Barre chord

Chords and scales can be shown in a fretbox, like this. Grey circles show root notes of the key, Black circles show other scale tones, and numbers give the fingering. Strings marked 'O' are open notes, and those marked 'X' should not be played.

TREBLE CLEF AND TABLATURE EXAMPLE

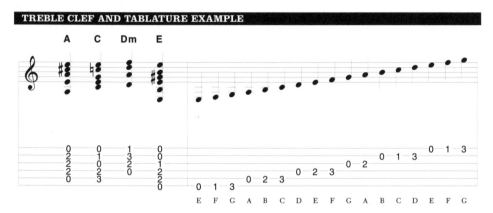

The treble clef (top) shows the musical pitches of the notes you play. The lines (bottom) correspond to the strings of the guitar; the bass E (sixth) string is shown at the bottom. The numbers show the position

where you fret the note – a zero means play the open string. This example shows four simple chords represented in tab, plus some of the note names available on the first few frets.

BEND UP/DOWN	**REPICK**	**PRE-BEND**	**HAMMER-ON**	**PULL-OFF**
		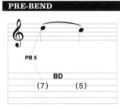		
Fret the start note (here, the 5th fret) and bend up to the pitch of the bracketed note, before releasing again.	Bend up to the pitch shown in brackets, then pick the note again while holding the bent note at the pitch shown.	Bend the note up (from the 5th fret) to the pitch of the 7th fret note before you pick it, then pick and release.	Pick the note at the fifth fret, then sound the seventh fret using the fretboard hand without repicking the note.	Fret the note at the seventh fret and also the fifth with another finger, then pull the finger off to sound the note.

SLIDE (GLISSANDO)	**FRETBOARD MUTES**	**PALM MUTES**	**RIGHT-HAND TAPPING**	**LEFT-HAND TAPPING**
	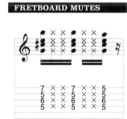			
Pick the 7th fret note, then slide the finger down to the 5th without repicking.	Notes marked with an X should be damped using the fingers of the fretting hand.	Mute by resting the fleshy part of the picking hand on the strings near the bridge.	Tap onto the the circled 12th fret notes using one finger of the picking hand.	Sound the notes marked with a square with the fretting hand.

NATURAL HARMONICS	**PINCHED HARMONICS**	**VIBRATO**	**WHAMMY BAR DIVE**	**WHAMMY BAR BENDS**
	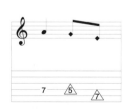			
Touch the string over the fret indicated, pick it firmly, and remove the picking hand.	Fret where shown, but dig into the string with the side of the thumb as you pick.	Wobble the note with the fretting hand, usually with an up-and-down motion.	Pick the note, then depress the whammy bar so that the pitch of the note descends.	Using the bar, bend the note up or down to the pitches indicated in the notation.

Back In Black (AC/DC)
(A.Young/M. Young/Johnson) J. Albert & Son Pty Ltd.

1. Full performance
2. Backing track only

White Room (Cream)
(Bruce/Brown) Warner Chappell Music Ltd.

3. Full performance
4. Backing track only

Sultans Of Swing (Dire Straits)
(Knopfler) Rondor Music (London) Ltd.

5. Intro, then verses 1 & 2
6. The main chorus riff
7. Verses 3 & 4, into chorus 2
8. Verse 5, into chorus 3
9. The first complete guitar solo, followed by chorus 4
10. Verse 6, then chorus 5
11. The second guitar solo
12. Backing track only

Johnny B Goode (Chuck Berry)
(Berry) Jewel Music Publishing Company Ltd.

13. 12-bar intro
14. Verse and chorus 12-bar sequence
15. The solo in full
16. Backing track only

Wishing Well (Free)
(Rodgers/Kirke/Yamauchi/Bundrick/Kossoff) Island Music Ltd.

17 a. Intro riff
    b. Verse accompaniment
18 a. Chorus, without repeats
    b. Lead and rhythm parts for the bridge
19 a. First guitar solo
    b. Last chorus and outro solo
20. Backing track only

Samba Pa Ti (Santana)
(Santana) BMG Music Publishing Ltd.

21. Full performance
22. Backing track only

MCPS

Enhanced CD: The audio on the Enhanced CD can be played on either your Hi-fi or multimedia PC. If you are on the Internet and want to browse the World's largest selections of sheet music, simply place the CD in your CD-Rom drive and follow the on-screen instructions.